A Duck, Duck, Porcupine! Book

That's My Book!

And Other Stories

Salina Yoon

SCHOLASTIC INC.

For Penguin

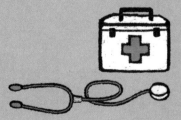

ISBN 978-1-338-34260-4

12 11 10 9 8 7 6 5 4 3 2 1   18 19 20 21 22 23

Printed in the U.S.A.   40

First Scholastic printing, September 2018

Art created digitally using Adobe Photoshop
Typeset in Cronos Pro
Book design by Salina Yoon and Jeanette Levy

Three Short Stories

One
That's My Book!

Two
Let's Have a Talent Show!

Three
Dress-Like-a-Pirate Day

One

That's My Book!

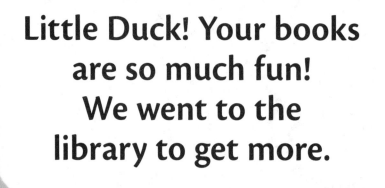

Little Duck! Your books
are so much fun!
We went to the
library to get more.

Two

Let's Have a Talent Show!

Three

Dress-Like-a-
Pirate Day

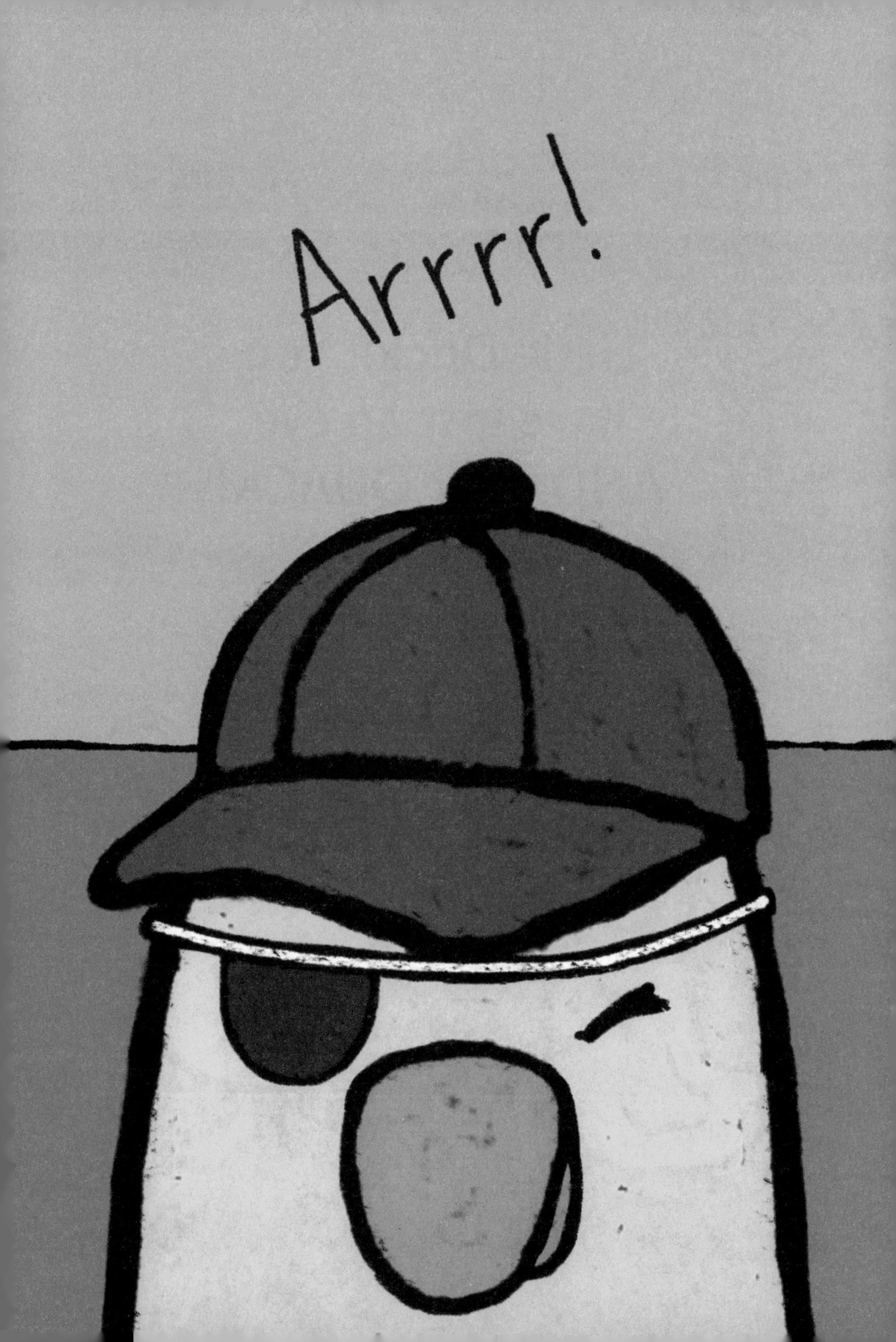
Arrrr!

Arrrrrr!